Run!

Helen Roberts • **Jonatronix**

OXFORD

UNIVERSITY PRESS

CODE Control Update:

My name is **CODE**. I am the computer that controls **Micro World**. **Team X** and **Mini** are trying to get the **CODE keys** and rescue **Macro Marvel**. My **BITEs** must stop them!

Team X are in:
Bugtastic zone

Team X

Mini

CODE key

BITE

Bugtastic cameras

CAMERA 1 — REC

Team X and Mini are on the Big Bug.

CAMERA 2 — REC

A bug jumps at Cat. Max stops it.

CAMERA 3 — REC

An ant grabs Tiger.

CAMERA 4 — REC

Tiger is stuck. Cat helps him.

Status: Tiger and Cat run from the BITE.

Before you read

Sound checker

Say the sounds.

j v w z
zz x y qu

Tricky words

he	was
she	you
they	my
are	

Sound spotter

Blend the sounds.

j	u	m	p

b	u	zz

w	i	ll

f	i	x

z	a	p

y	e	ll	s

v	i	c	t	i	m	s

qu	i	t

Into the zone

Will the BITE spot Cat
and Tiger?

The BITE spots Cat and Tiger. It is cross.

The BITE is fast.
It will not stop.

You are my victims!

Cat and Tiger are in a fix. They will not quit.

Where next?

It can not see Cat and Tiger. They win!

That was a top plan, Cat!

Tiger spots a pit.
He yells to Cat.
She is in a jam.

Cat!

Help!

12

Cat and Tiger run back to the Big Bug.

Max, Ant and Mini are not on the ride.

Now you have read ...
Run!

Text checker

How do you know that the BITE is cross?

MITE fun

How did Tiger help Cat get out of the pit? Tell the story in your own words.

This is not the end!